SELF-HELPING MYSELF

A GUIDED JOURNAL to HELP YOU
DISCOVER & UNCOVER WHO YOU ARE
and HOW YOU GOT HERE

EM&
FRIENDS™

I, ─────────────,

HEREBY GRANT MYSELF FULL PERMISSION

to become the kind of person who not only **owns** a journal, but also the kind of person who **writes** in a journal. I give myself permission to not hold back for any excuse disguised as a "reason," like not having a cool pen with me or not liking the way my handwriting looks. I understand that my private thoughts and feelings are valid and don't permanently define me. I know that as a human being, I am capable of changing my mind and surprising myself. I give myself permission to let go of resentments, fears, and confusion. I can invite peace, encouragement, and forward momentum into my life. Or not. I get to decide what I journal about. Yay.

THERE IS NO WRONG WAY to KEEP A JOURNAL.

Signed: ─────────────── Date:────────

WHERE ARE THINGS AT?
A Self-Evaluation

*Before you begin to journal, consider taking some time to get
warmed up by answering the following questions.*

What is your life like right now, in this moment?
What is your daily routine, and how do you feel about it?

....

....

....

....

....

....

....

....

....

....

....

....

How do you feel about the direction your life is heading in right now?

....

....

....

....

....

....

....

....

What routines/responsibilities or commitments do you deal with on a regular basis that you'd like to let go of (even if that doesn't feel possible)?

....

....

....

....

....

....

....

....

What makes you happy? And we don't mean rainbows and puppies,
although those things are seriously happiness-inducing—but rather, what
things do you do regularly, just for yourself, that make you feel fulfilled?
What activities do you look forward to? What do you make time for?

....

....

....

....

....

....

....

Let your mind wander for a few minutes. Think about what makes you special.
Make a list of everything that comes to mind. Don't be shy! This is all you.

....

....

....

....

....

....

....

....

What would it take for you to make some significant changes in the areas of your life where you feel you need improvement?

....

....

....

....

....

....

....

....

....

....

....

....

....

....

....

ON a SCALE of 1 to 10, with 10 BEING CLOSE to IDEAL and 1 BEING the WORST YOU CAN IMAGINE, RATE the FOLLOWING AREAS of YOUR LIFE AS OF RIGHT NOW, TODAY.

Date:_____

My LIFE OVERALL: _____

My PHYSICAL HEALTH:_____

My MENTAL HEALTH: _____

My CLOSE RELATIONSHIPS: _____

My DAILY WORK/CAREER:_____

My CREATIVITY: _____

My USE OF FREE TIME: _____

My FINANCES: _____

My INNER WORLD: _____

My PROGRESS TOWARD FUTURE DREAMS and/or DESIRES: _____

OK, phew. Now it's time to write yourself a little pep talk! If this feels hard, pretend you're talking to your best friend. What would you say to encourage them to work toward the life they envision for themselves?

....

....

....

....

....

....

....

....

....

....

....

....

....

....

....

TO GET GOING   TO STAY PUT

TO BE LOST   TO KNOW ABSOLUTELY

TO START AGAIN   TO IGNORE LOGIC

— CONSIDER THIS —
YOUR PERMISSION SLIP

TO BE HAPPY   TO BE SAD   TO FEEL LONELY

TO ENJOY BEING ALONE   TO SAY YES   TO SAY NO

TO CRY   TO FEEL GOOD   TO DO NOTHING

TO BE YOURSELF   TO BE IN LOVE WITH YOURSELF   TO CHANGE

TO DO, BE, OR HAVE WHATEVER YOU WANT.

THOUGHT-STARTER
— Questions —

Use the pages that follow to answer some or all of the questions here. Or none! You do you.

How do you define hope? What does it mean to you?
What do you hope for the most?

What do you want your life to look like one year from now? How do you want to feel when you wake up in the morning and go to bed at night? What do you want your work to be like? How do you feel in (and about) your body? How are your relationships? What have you let go of? What have you accomplished? How about five years from now? Ten years?

Make a list of dreams that have come true for you so far. Write about what made these dreams possible. Who helped you? How did you help yourself?

What are you afraid of and why? What can you do about it?

What do you want for yourself that feels impossible? Can you think of three things that can help you get there bit by bit— or leap by leap?

Date: ....

Date: ....

Date: ....

IN JAPAN, BROKEN OBJECTS are OFTEN REPAIRED WITH GOLD. The FLAW IS SEEN AS a UNIQUE PIECE OF the OBJECT'S HISTORY, WHICH ADDS TO ITS BEAUTY.

CONSIDER THIS
WHEN YOU FEEL BROKEN.

THOUGHT-STARTER
— Questions —

Use the pages that follow to answer some or all of the questions here. Or none! You do you.

How have the challenges and pain you've experienced helped to shape who you are?

◆

Can you identify any gifts that came from those experiences? Maybe a different perspective, increased empathy, or a sense of purpose? People you ended up meeting?

◆

At what point in your life did you feel like the truest and most honest version of you? If it's not right now, what has changed?

◆

When you're feeling good about your life, how can you tell? Does your body or mind send you signals that alert you? Do you get feedback from others commenting on your disposition or energy?

◆

Do you struggle to allow yourself to feel good, or to celebrate your successes? If so, why do you think this is?

◆

What would your optimal self do when you're feeling ... happy, depressed, confused, angry?

◆◆◆

Date: ....

Date: ....

Date: ....

Date: ....

'HOME' is NOT a GEOGRAPHICAL PLACE for ME, BUT, MORE OFTEN, a PERSON. And THUS, I CAN HONESTLY SAY: I HAVE HOMES ALL OVER the WORLD.

Elizabeth Gilbert

THOUGHT-STARTER
— Questions —

*Use the pages that follow to answer some or all of the
questions here. Or none! You do you.*

Who feels like home to you?
What about them makes you feel this way?

◆

Looking back on the ways you've interacted with your family
members in the past, what would you like to be forgiven for?

◆

Is there someone in your family who you feel like you can't forgive,
or who you'd like to forgive? How would your life be different if you
forgave that person? (Forgiveness doesn't mean what happened
was okay, and it doesn't mean you need to have a relationship with
that person. Forgiveness allows you to release the weight of the
resentment you're carrying, resulting in more internal peace.)

◆

What does the concept of family mean to you?

◆

Who are your most treasured family members? What's especially
wonderful about each of them?

◆

Make a list of the habits or beliefs you've learned from
your family members or family dynamic. Which ones serve you,
and which ones don't?

◆

Who do you consider family, even though you are not related? Why?

Date: ....

Date: ....

IF YOU'RE LUCKY, THERE ARE PEOPLE in YOUR LIFE WHO ARE WILLING to LISTEN TO YOU TALK IN CIRCLES ABOUT THE SAME BULLS*!T FOR LIKE ELEVEN YEARS and STILL CHOOSE to HANG OUT WITH YOU.

THOUGHT-STARTER
— Questions —

Use the pages that follow to answer some or all of the questions here. Or none! You do you.

If you're missing the kind of friendship you wish you had in your life, write a job description for the type of friend you're seeking.

◆

What makes you a good friend to others? What do you give back to them? What do you offer?

◆

Sometimes we outgrow people, or just move in different directions. Are you holding onto any old friendships that no longer serve you? Think about those relationships. What did they once give you? How have you changed since then?

◆

Has a friend ever broken up with you out of the blue? Reflect upon that time and what you learned about yourself while it was happening. What do you think about it now?

◆

Make a list of all the people you've ever considered a best friend, and what made each person important to you.

◆

Do you make friends easily? If so, what about you is approachable? If not, why do you think this might be?

◆◆◆

Date: ....

Date: ....

Date: ....

Date: ....

Date: ....

LOVING YOURSELF is a PRACTICE, JUST LIKE YOGA. NOBODY EVER got GOOD at YOGA by BELIEVING IN IT. you HAVE TO DO IT. EVEN WHEN IT'S HARD. ESPECIALLY WHEN IT'S HARD.

THOUGHT-STARTER
— Questions —

Use the pages that follow to answer some or all of the
questions here. Or none! You do you.

Think back to a time in your life when you were going through something
scary or rough. Remember how you felt back then, and write that version
of yourself a letter, expressing love and encouragement. With your current
perspective, lovingly say what you needed to hear at that time.

◆

Make a list of everything you can think of that you love. Leave nothing out!
Include everything from your favorite thing to eat for breakfast to books that
are meaningful to you. Keep adding to it as time goes on and you discover
new loves. When you feel lost, come back to this list, read it, and try to add
one new thing to it.

◆

How do you express love to the people you care about most?

◆

How do you receive love from people who care about you? Do you struggle to
receive love, or to feel like you deserve love? Why?

◆

What's your favorite love song? Copy the lyrics into your journal, and write
about what they mean to you and why. If you're feeling extra creative, rewrite
them to fit your life, or a love you've experienced. (Don't worry about rhyming.)

◆

Do you have any patterns around love that you repeat again and again?
Why do you think they've become patterns? Would you like to change them?
If so, how? Are you happy with your patterns? If so, why?

Date: ....

Date: ....

Date: ....

MY HOBBIES?
THEY INCLUDE
READING, BRUNCH,
and WINNING
IMAGINARY
ARGUMENTS WITH
PEOPLE FROM
THE PAST.

THOUGHT-STARTER
— Questions —

Use the pages that follow to answer some or all of the questions here. Or none! You do you.

How do you like to spend your leisure time, and why?

◆

What natural abilities and skills do you have that contribute to what you are interested in? Do you have these gifts in common with other people you know?

◆

What benefits do you receive from your hobbies?
How do they fulfill you?

◆

If you won an all-expenses-paid, two-week trip to anywhere in the world, but you were required to spend it doing something creative, where would you go? What would you learn? How do you think it would change your life?

◆

If you could gain a world-renowned expertise in any discipline, what would you choose to focus on and why? Pretend you can't make money doing it. Does that affect your decision?

◆

Write about a time you were moved by someone else's art. Maybe it was a movie that made you think, a museum visit that filled your heart with unexpected emotion, or a simple meal made by the best cook in your family. How did the experience come about, and how did it affect you?

◆◆◆

Date: ....

Date: ....

THE PATRIARCHY ISN'T GOING TO FIGHT ITSELF.

THOUGHT-STARTER
— Questions —

Use the pages that follow to answer some or all of the questions here. Or none! You do you.

Finish this sentence: "If I were in charge of my government, the first five changes I'd implement would be..."

◆

So much of what happens in the world can be painful to witness. When it all feels like too much and you feel overwhelmed, what is that like for you? Write about how it feels in your body. What can you do to alleviate those fears and feelings?

◆

Make a list of things you think are really wonderful about the world at large. For example: those glass igloo hotels that let you lie in bed and see the northern lights. Another example: Flowers exist. Flowers! They grow everywhere! *Even from the cracks in the pavement!*

◆

What is good about the community you live in? What would you like to see change? How are you involved in your community?

◆

If you were granted three wishes that could only benefit your country, what would you wish for? Why?

Date: ....

Date: ....

I'M SO THANKFUL FOR ALL of the PAST VERSIONS of MYSELF WHO DIDN'T GIVE UP, EVEN WHEN THEY REALLY, REALLY WANTED TO.

THOUGHT-STARTER
— Questions —

Use the pages that follow to answer some or all of the questions here. Or none! You do you.

Write three thank-you notes: one to your past self, one to your present-day self, and one to your future self. Let yourself know what you appreciate about you, acknowledge your hard work, and pat yourself on the back.

—

Spend a whole day keeping track of every single thing you could possibly feel gratitude for—from waking up in clean sheets to seeing the moon and stars before you go to sleep. Keep your running list here and look at it when you've had a hard day. Take comfort in all of the good things in your life, big and small and tiny.

—

What are the best presents you've ever received? Who gave them to you? What makes them so awesome? Were they material objects? Acts of kindness? Both?

—

Go out of your way to acknowledge at least three people you interact with on a semi-regular basis. Maybe your dog-sitter, a friendly neighbor, or the parking-lot attendant at work. Thank them for what they do. Be specific. Record their reaction here, and how it made you feel to express your gratitude toward them.

—

What do people say it is that makes you special to them? What do people often thank you for? What are you really good at that helps others, or makes people happy? Write about these talents (yes, they are talents!) and say why you're thankful for them.

Date: ....

Date: ....

LESSON FROM a MOUNTAIN:

IT IS OUR BIRTHRIGHT to REST in SILENCE, TAKE UP SPACE, and LOOK FREAKING MAJESTIC.

THOUGHT-STARTER
— Questions —

Use the pages that follow to answer some or all of the questions here. Or none! You do you.

Recall a painful lesson you've learned.
How has it impacted the way you live your life now?

◆

If you were giving a graduation commencement speech to people younger than you, what are the three most important things you'd tell them about living a good life, based on what you know right now?

◆

What's the best advice, and the worst advice, you've ever gotten?
Who or what told you those things?

◆

What lessons do you seem to need to learn over and over? Why do you think you're so resistant to learning them?

◆

What assumptions, beliefs, and old stories do you carry around with you that are based on conclusions you drew from past events? These could be things about yourself, such as "Nobody is interested in what I have to say." They could also be about the world (e.g., "People only care about getting ahead."). Which of these do you most want to let go of?

◆

Pretend you are near the end of your life. Look back on how you've lived, and what kind of person you were. What would you forgive yourself for? Would you regret anything? What would make you feel proud of yourself?

◆◆◆

Date: ....

Date: ....

Date: ....

WHERE ARE THINGS GOING?
Intentions for Moving Forward

If you've gotten to this part of your journal, it might mean you've filled every page with your thoughts and feelings and realizations and discoveries. Or it could mean you're the kind of person who skips straight to the end of the story, and you kind of just want to wrap this whole project up already. Either way, you get to decide what feels best to you. This is where we encourage you to consider what comes next in the Story of You.

What is your life like right now, in this moment? What is your daily routine, and how do you feel about it? How is it different from when you started this journal?

....

....

....

....

....

....

....

....

....

....

....

What has changed for you and what feels different?

....

....

....

....

....

....

....

....

....

....

....

....

....

....

....

....

Reflecting on everything you've written, fill in the blanks:

What really surprised me about this process was: ....
....

One of my biggest takeaways from journaling is: ....
....

I've let go of: ....
....

I've reconsidered: ....
....
....

I've learned: ....
....
....

I've accepted: ....
....
....

I am struggling to accept: ....
....
....

Moving forward, what do you want your life to feel like?
How do you want to **feel** in your body, mind, and heart?

What tools or resources can you use to help make this intended
new reality a real-life thing?

....

....

....

....

....

....

....

....

What did you enjoy most about journaling?

....

....

....

....

....

....

....

ON a SCALE of 1 to 10, with 10 BEING CLOSE to IDEAL and 1 BEING the WORST YOU CAN IMAGINE, RATE the FOLLOWING AREAS of YOUR LIFE AS OF RIGHT NOW, TODAY.

Date:_____

My LIFE OVERALL: _____

My PHYSICAL HEALTH: _____

My MENTAL HEALTH: _____

My CLOSE RELATIONSHIPS: _____

My DAILY WORK/CAREER: _____

My CREATIVITY: _____

My USE OF FREE TIME: _____

My FINANCES: _____

My INNER WORLD: _____

My PROGRESS TOWARD FUTURE DREAMS and/ or DESIRES: _____

Okay, this is the (really) fun part . . . YAY. Write a pep talk to yourself about how you want to move forward. Think about the work you still want to do and offer yourself encouragement and acceptance to continue on. You are worth it! Don't hold back— really lay it on thick. It might feel cheesy or awkward. Do it anyway.

....

....

....

....

....

....

....

....

....

....

....

....

....

I ACTUALLY COMPLETED A JOURNAL *Award*

THIS AMAZING ACHIEVEMENT AWARD
IS HEREBY ISSUED to ME,

_____

FOR the MIGHTY TASK OF
ACTUALLY COMPLETING A JOURNAL.

I HONOR MYSELF and MY ACCOMPLISHMENT
on THIS ___ DAY OF _____, in the YEAR OF ____.

I AM A PERSON
WHO JOURNALS NOW.

_____
SIGNED